# Contents

Girls and boys come out to play . . . 2
Go to bed early . . . 3
Goodness gracious! . . . 4
Gregory Griggs . . . 5
The mocking bird . . . 6
I wonder . . . 7
Christmas secrets . . . 8
Jump or jiggle . . . 9
Here is the Nose that smelled something sweet . . . 10
The tiger . . . 12
Would you dare? . . . 13
Three mice . . . 14
One, two, buckle my shoe . . . 15
One two Anancy . . . 16
Mother Alligator's advice to her children . . . 16

# Girls and boys come out to play

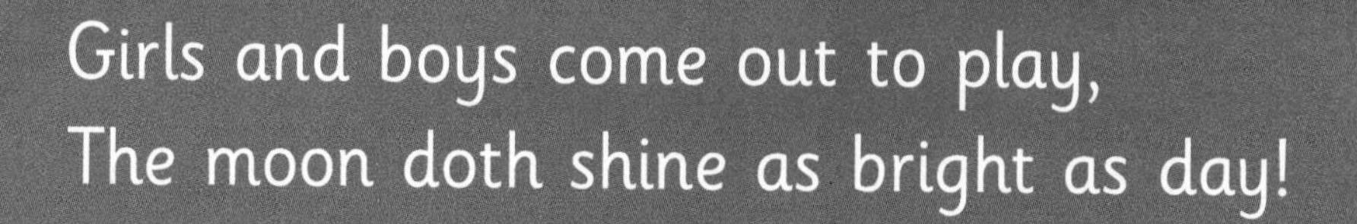

Girls and boys come out to play,
The moon doth shine as bright as day!

Leave your supper and leave your sleep,
Come with your playfellows into the street.

Come with a whistle, come with a call,
Come with a goodwill or not at all.

Up the ladder and down the wall,
A halfpenny roll will serve us all.

You find milk and I'll find flour,
And we'll have a pudding in half an hour.

# Go to bed early

Go to bed early – wake up with joy,
Go to bed late – cross girl or boy.
Go to bed early – ready for play,
Go to bed late – moping all day.
Go to bed early – no pains or ills,
Go to bed late – doctors and pills.
Go to bed early – grow very tall,
Go to bed late – stay very small.

# Goodness gracious!

Goodness gracious, fiddle dee dee!
Somebody's grandmother out at sea!

Just where the breakers begin to bound
Somebody's grandmother bobbing around.

Up on the shore the people shout,
"Give us a hand and we'll pull you out!"

"No!" says granny. "I'm right as rain,
And I'm going to go on till I get to Spain."

*Margaret Mahy*

## Gregory Griggs

Gregory Griggs, Gregory Griggs,
Had twenty-seven different wigs.
He wore them up, he wore them down,
To please the people of the town.
He wore them east, he wore them west,
But he never could tell which he loved
the best.

# The mocking bird

Hush, little baby, don't say a word,
Papa's going to buy you a mocking bird.

If the mocking bird won't sing,
Papa's going to buy you a diamond ring.

If the diamond ring turns to brass,
Papa's going to buy you a looking-glass.

If the looking-glass gets broke,
Papa's going to buy you a billy-goat.

If that billy-goat runs away,
Papa's going to buy you another today.

# I wonder

I wonder why the grass is green,
And why the wind is never seen?

Who taught the birds to build a nest,
And told the trees to take a rest?

O, when the moon is not quite round,
Where can the missing bit be found?

Who lights the stars, when they blow out,
And makes the lightning flash about?

Who paints the rainbow in the sky,
And hangs the fluffy clouds so high?

Why is it now, do you suppose,
That Dad won't tell me, if he knows?

*Jeannie Kirby*

# Christmas secrets

Secrets long and secrets wide,
brightly wrapped and tightly tied,

Secrets fat and secrets thin,
boxed and sealed and hidden in,

Some that rattle, some that squeak,
some that caution, 'Do Not Peek' ...

Hurry, Christmas, get here first,
get here fast ... before we burst.

*Aileen Fisher*

# Jump or jiggle

Frogs jump
Caterpillars hump

Worms wiggle
Bugs jiggle

Rabbits hop
Horses clop

Snakes slide
Seagulls glide

Mice creep
Deer leap

Puppies bounce
Kittens pounce

Lions stalk –
But –
I walk!

*Evelyn Beyer*

# Here is the Nose that smelled something sweet

Here is the **Nose** that smelled something sweet
And led the search for something to eat

Here are the **Feet** that followed the **Nose**
Around the kitchen on ten **Tiptoes**

Here are the **Eyes** that looked high and low
Till they spotted six pans sitting all in a row

Here are the **Arms** that reached up high
To bring down a fresh-baked blueberry pie

Here is the **Mouth** that opened up wide
Here are the **Hands** that put pie inside

Here is the **Tongue** that licked the tin
And lapped up the juice running down the **Chin**

Here is the **Stomach** that growled for more
Here are the **Legs** that ran for the door

Here are the **Ears** that heard a whack
Here is the **Bottom** that felt a smack!

*Clyde Watson*

## The tiger

A tiger going for a stroll
Met an old man and ate him whole.

The old man shouted, and he thumped.
The tiger's stomach churned and bumped.

The other tigers said: "Now really
We hear your breakfast much too clearly."

The moral is, he should have chewed.
It does no good to bolt one's food.

*Edward Lucie-Smith*

# Would you dare?

Would you dare, would you dare
To dance round the room
    with a big shaggy bear?

Will you try, will you try
To wipe a tear from an elephant's eye?

Could you smile, could you smile
As you sat on the back of a long crocodile?

Would you ever, would you ever
Tickle a lion with a yellow feather?

Will you make, will you make
Friends with a slithering ten foot long snake?

*Barbara Ireson*

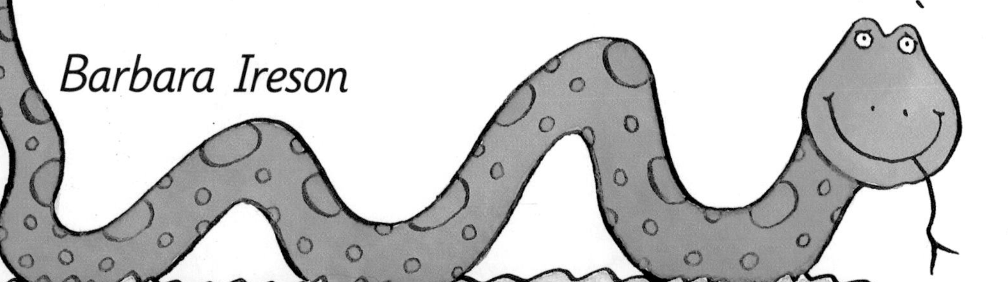

# Three mice

Three little mice walked into town,
Their coats were grey, and their eyes were brown.

Three little mice went down the street,
With woolwork slippers upon their feet.

Three little mice sat down to dine
On curranty bread and gooseberry wine.

Three little mice ate on and on
Till every crumb of the bread was gone.

Three little mice, when the feast was done,
Crept home quietly, one by one.

Three little mice went straight to bed,
And dreamt of crumbly, curranty bread.

*Charlotte Druitt Cole*

# One, two, buckle my shoe

One, two,
Buckle my shoe.
Three, four,
Knock at the door,
Five, six,
Pick up sticks,

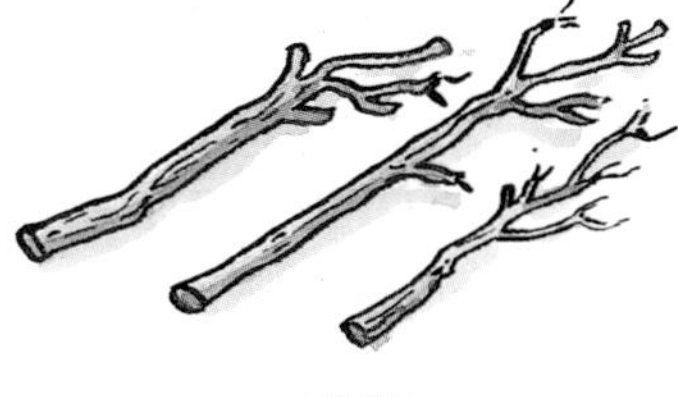

Seven, eight,
Lay them straight,
Nine, ten,
A good fat hen,
Eleven, twelve,
Dig and delve,

Thirteen, fourteen,
Maids a-courting,
Fifteen, sixteen,
Maids in the kitchen,

Seventeen, eighteen,
Maids a-waiting,

Nineteen, twenty,
My plate's empty.

## One two Anancy

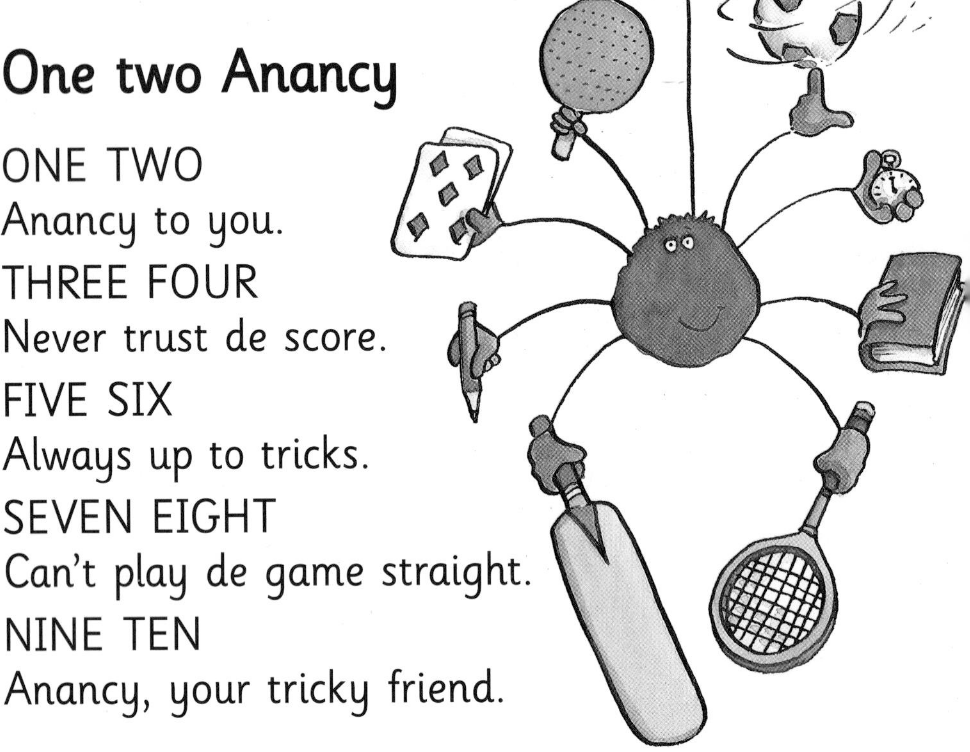

ONE TWO
Anancy to you.
THREE FOUR
Never trust de score.
FIVE SIX
Always up to tricks.
SEVEN EIGHT
Can't play de game straight.
NINE TEN
Anancy, your tricky friend.

*John Agard*

## Mother Alligator's advice to her children

Don't eat too much sweet
You'll spoil your lovely teeth.

Don't touch jelly or treacle
Stick to eating people.

*John Agard*